JOKE BOOK

9 YEAR OLD EDITION

TRY NOT TO LAUGH CHALLENGE™

Try Not To Laugh Challenge
BONUS PLAY

Join our Joke Club and get the Bonus Play PDF!

Simply send us an email to:

TNTLPublishing@gmail.com

and you will get the following:

• **10 Hilarious, Bonus Jokes**

• **An entry in our Monthly Giveaway of a $50 Amazon Gift card!**

We draw a new winner each month and will contact you via email!

Good luck!

WELCOME TO THE
TRY NOT TO LAUGH CHALLENGE!

RULES OF THE GAME:

★ Grab a friend or family member, a pen/pencil, and your comedic skills! Determine who will be "Jokester 1" and "Jokester 2".

★ Take turns reading the jokes aloud to each other, and check the box next to each joke you get a laugh from! Each laugh box is worth 1 point, and the pages are labeled to instruct and guide when it is each player's turn.

★ Once you have both completed telling jokes in the round, tally up your laugh points and mark it down on each score page! There is a total of 10 Rounds.

★ Play as many rounds as you like! Once you reach the last round, Round 10, tally up ALL points from the previous rounds to determine who is the CHAMPION LAUGH MASTER!

★ Round 11 - The Tie-Breaker Round.

In the event of a tie, proceed to Round 11. This round will be 'Winner Takes All!', so whoever scores more laugh points in this round alone, is crowned the CHAMPION LAUGH MASTER!

TIP: Use an expressive voice, facial expressions, and even silly body movement to really get the most out of each joke and keep the crowd laughing!

Now, it's time to play!

ROUND 1

JOKESTER 1

What contests are most common in sorcery schools?

SPELL-ing Bees!

C
LAUC

What's a pilot's favorite snack?

Wings!

C
LAUC

What do you call your father when he turns into a zombie?

'The Walking Dad.'

C
LAUC

Why wouldn't the picky spider eat wings?

He had only ate legs. (Eight)

C
LAUC

What do cats put on their spaghetti?

PURR-mesan cheese.

 LAUGH

What did the socks say to the feet?

"We've got you covered!"

 LAUGH

How can you tell if your car has a cold?

They honk ATCHOO!

LAUGH

What do you call a boring underwater tour?

A SNORE-kel.

 LAUGH

Pass the book to Jokester 2! →

What do you call a pig who lives in Toronto?

Canadian Bacon.

C
LAUC

Why did the Star Wars pilot never fly?

He wanted to be a sky-WALKER!

C
LAUC

Why does Snow White not have an iPhone?

C
LAUC

She tries to stay away from Apple products...

Why did the Veterinarian need ar umbrella?

It was raining cats and dogs!

C
LAUC

What do you call an insect that practices gymnastics?
A TUMBLE-bee!

 LAUGH

What is an owl's favorite type of jewelry?
HOO-p earrings.

 LAUGH

What do you call an animal that likes to hang out?
A chin-CHILLER!

LAUGH

What is a snake's favorite board game?
RATTLE-ship!

 LAUGH

Time to add up your points! →

SCORE BOARD

Add up each Jokester's laugh points
for this round!

JOKESTER 1

$$\frac{\quad}{\text{Total}} \; /8$$

JOKESTER 2

$$\frac{\quad}{\text{Total}} \; /8$$

ROUND WINNER

ROUND

2

What is a priest's favorite football play?

The Hail Mary!

LAU(

How do you download a shark?

One mega-BITE at a time!

LAU(

Why did the monster eat the chandelier?

He wanted a LIGHT meal!

LAU(

What kind of entertainment do peas like?

POD-casts!

LAU(

 **JOKESTER 1**

Why didn't the cell phone ever order a meal?

It was already full on APPS!

 LAUGH

What weapon did the librarian use to scare off the thief?

A book club!

○ LAUGH

Why did the bus driver drive past the school, instead of stopping?

She wanted the kids to PASS their classes.

○ LAUGH

How do you keep from stinking up the mountain?

Wear your SKI-oderant!

 LAUGH

Pass the book to Jokester 2! ➔

Why are architects so popular?

They are always building bridges!

LAUC

Why did the man leave books in the garage?

He wanted to drive a SMART car!

LAUC

What did Yogi Bear say to Booboo?

"Thank you for BEAR-ing with me!"

LAUC

What is it called when fluffy dogs play in the rain?

Poodle jumping! (Puddle)

LAU

Who is known for being the loudest person at a hotel?

The Bellboy!

LAUGH

What do you call baby lions on top of mama lion?

A backpack!

LAUGH

What do you call a vacation with new glasses?

Sight-seeing!

LAUGH

Why was the basketball player so bad?

He TRAVELS way too much!

LAUGH

Time to add up your points! →

SCORE BOARD

Add up each Jokester's laugh points for this round!

JOKESTER 1

/8

Total

JOKESTER 2

/8

Total

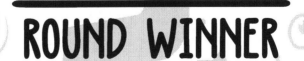

ROUND WINNER

ROUND

3

What do you call a baseball player with chocolate chips?

Cookie batter.

LAUGH

Why didn't the little snake go to the big animal festival?

It didn't be-LONG!

LAUG

What kind of shirts do sheep wear?

Goat-Tee's.

LAUG

What's a ghost's favorite type o wood?

Bam-BOO!

LAU

 **JOKESTER 1**

What kind of makeup do horses use?

NEIGH-belline!

 LAUGH

Knock Knock.
Who's there?
Saint.
Saint, who?
Saint the time for questions!
Open that door!

LAUGH

Why did no one use the jaguar's cell phone?

His signal was always SPOT-ty!

LAUGH

What state borrows a lot?

Iowa you!

 LAUGH

Pass the book to Jokester 2! ➜

What's another name for a mouse teacher?

A Cheese Grader!

LAUGH

What tests do dummies study for?

Crash tests!

LAUGH

What did the cowboy ask the bronco?

"Can you give me a few BUCKS?"

LAUG

What do you call a lightbulb family reunion?

A flash mob!

LAUG

What kind of shoes do plumbers fix?

Clogs!

 LAUGH

What kind of sandwiches do cavemen eat?

CLUB sandwiches!

 LAUGH

Why is packing things up good for self-defense?

You learn how to box!

☐ LAUGH

What is an insect's favorite sport?

Cricket!

 LAUGH

Time to add up your points! →

SCORE BOARD

Add up each Jokester's laugh points
for this round!

JOKESTER 1

$\dfrac{\quad\quad}{\text{Total}}$ /8

JOKESTER 2

$\dfrac{\quad\quad}{\text{Total}}$ /8

ROUND WINNER

ROUND 4

What did the sheet say to the mattress?

"Don't worry, I've got you covered."

LAU◖

What does the untamed desert horse hate?

Rains. (Reins)

LAU◖

Why were dinosaurs so smelly?

They were ex-STINK-ed.

LAU◖

What did the butcher say, when meeting the steak for the first time?

"Nice to finally MEAT you!"

LAU◖

 **JOKESTER 1**

Why was the fried chicken afraid to cross the street?

There was a spork in the road! ☐ LAUGH

Who won the neckwear contest?

It was a tie! ☐ LAUGH

Why was the news reporter always stopping boats?

Because he's an ANCHOR! ☐ LAUGH

What has one eye and knows everything?

An en-CYCLOP-edia! ☐ LAUGH

Pass the book to Jokester 2! ➜

Why was the tree so tired?

His friends would never LEAF!

C
LAU

What is the opposite of a 'light Ford'?

'A heavy Chevy!'

C
LAU

Why did the baseball player go to the gas station?

For a shortstop!

C
LAU

What method does the superhero use to study?

FLASH-cards!

C
LAU

How do poodles steer canoes?

With dog paddles!

LAUGH

Why did the student's knee hurt?

They fell during the field-TRIP!

LAUGH

What type of furniture makes you really gassy?

The bean bag... EW!

LAUGH

Why was the car always working?

LAUGH

It never got a BRAKE!

Time to add up your points! →

SCORE BOARD

Add up each Jokester's laugh points for this round!

JOKESTER 1

$$\frac{/8}{\text{Total}}$$

JOKESTER 2

$$\frac{/8}{\text{Total}}$$

ROUND WINNER

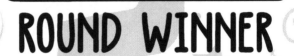

ROUND

5

What play was the jelly always making in basketball?

JAM DUNKS! (SLAM)

LAUC

Why did the chef include a soccer shoe in his soup?

To give it a little KICK!

LAUC

How can you tell if a frog is obedient?

It does everything its TOAD to do!

LAUC

Why do mermaids do so well on cruises?

They already have their sea legs!

LAU

Why isn't there a big fashion market for chickens?

They prefer to wear HEN-me-downs! ☐ LAUGH

Why didn't the cool guy want to fly?

He just wanted to cruise, man. ☐ LAUGH

How do you wash clothes while in the ocean?

With TIDE-to-go! ☐ LAUGH

Why was the soccer player so determined?

He was always making GOALS! ☐ LAUGH

Pass the book to Jokester 2! →

What do you call a rock you find while playing basketball?

A GYM-stone! (Gemstone)

LAUG

Why are raindrops so bad at bowling?

They always go in the gutter!

LAUC

Why did the cow jump over the moon?

To get to the UDDER side.

LAUC

Can you play games of chance with an onion?

Yes, but you have to DICE it first.

LAUC

What kind of skirt does a math teacher like?

A two-two!

LAUGH

What kind of screen won't keep flies out?

Sunscreen!

LAUGH

What's the cure for a broken fingernail?

A mani-CURE!

LAUGH

Why did the robot buy new galoshes?

He wanted to be re-BOOT-ed!

LAUGH

Time to add up your points! →

SCORE BOARD

Add up each Jokester's laugh points for this round!

JOKESTER 1

$\dfrac{\qquad}{\text{Total}}$ /8

JOKESTER 2

$\dfrac{\qquad}{\text{Total}}$ /8

ROUND WINNER

ROUND 6

What do you call a nocturnal horse?

A night-MARE!

LAU

Why did the sea lion love to make jokes?

He loved being SEAL-ly!

LAU

Why did the duck regret his vacation to the beach?

The water wasn't all it was quacked up to be!

LAU

What do you do when a fruit dies?

BERRY it!

LAU

What did the police do to the coffee cup thief?

They took his MUG-shot.

☐ LAUGH

Why is lightning always a surprise?

Because it's SHOCK-ing!

☐ LAUGH

Why did the window make a great teacher?

It was always perfectly clear.

☐ LAUGH

What soap keeps you cool in the summer?

Hair conditioner.

☐ LAUGH

Pass the book to Jokester 2! →

41

What command do you give your dog when it gets hurt?

'Heal.'

○ LAUGH

What did the inspirational clock say every 60 minutes?

"This is hour time."

◖ LAUGH

Why did the bear sleep in the cold cave for winter?

He was hi-BURRR-nating.

◖ LAUGH

What did the skeptical fashion designer say about the new sewing machine?

"It seams good, but SEW what?"

◖ LAUGH

What's a painter's favorite insult?

"You BLUE it!"

☐ LAUGH

How do you keep your pastry recipes a secret?

You DONUT tell anyone!

☐ LAUGH

What do you call a stepped-on banana?

Fruit by the Foot.

☐ LAUGH

Why is dried fruit at the head of the class?

It's always RAISIN its hand!

☐ LAUGH

Time to add up your points! →

SCORE BOARD

Add up each Jokester's laugh points
for this round!

JOKESTER 1

/8

Total

JOKESTER 2

/8

Total

ROUND WINNER

ROUND
7

 **JOKESTER 1**

What did my grandfather use to walk away from the storm?

His HURRY-cane!

LAUC

What did they call James, after he moved to the rainforest?

'Jungle Jim!'

LAUC

Why did the gardener bring her plants to the car repairman?

They needed a SOIL change!

LAUC

Why are cosmetic stores good at writing fictional characters?

They MAKE-UP lots of people!

LAUC

 **JOKESTER 1**

Knock Knock.
Who's there?
Hula.
Hula, who?
I think you mean "Hula Hoop".

LAUGH ☐

What animal has the
best rhythm?

BEAT-les.

LAUGH ☐

Where does the celebrity
chef cook?

In a STEW-dio.

LAUGH ☐

How do dog sharks communicate?

Through shark bark!

LAUGH ☐

Pass the book to Jokester 2! →

What is a calendar's favorite tree?

MAY-ple!

LAUGH

Who do cats call when they are sick and need to go to the hospital?

A PURR-amedic!

LAUGH

Why did Shamoo take a sick day?

He wasn't feeling WHALE!

LAUG

Why do road trips with cops take so long?

LAUG

They always want to go to ar-REST stops!

48

Where do astronauts post their pictures?

SPACE-book!

 LAUGH

What is a musician's favorite type of bread?

A drum-ROLL!

 LAUGH

What kind of bird wears a toupee?

A Bald Eagle.

LAUGH

How do you find the right lipstick shade?

Use the lip GLOSS-ary!

 LAUGH

Time to add up your points! →

49

SCORE BOARD

Add up each Jokester's laugh points
for this round!

JOKESTER 1 $\dfrac{}{\text{Total}}$ 18

JOKESTER 2 $\dfrac{18}{\text{Total}}$

ROUND WINNER

ROUND 8

 **JOKESTER 1**

What do you call it when a batter hits a home run, but a bird catches it mid-air?

FOWL ball! (Foul)

LAUGH

Why are Captain Hook's pants so big?

To fit all of his pirate's booty!

LAUGH

Why was the TV feeling lonely?

It was in a REMOTE location!

LAUG

How do ants sing karaoke?

With a MICRO-phone!

LAUG

# JOKESTER 1

Why is the pirate so good at basketball?

His incredible HOOK shot!

LAUGH ☐

What did Dorothy say when she hit a home run?

"There's no BASE like home!"

LAUGH ☐

How do gymnasts respond to criticism?

They flip out!

LAUGH ☐

What game does the cheerleading squad like to play at parties?

Musical Cheers.

LAUGH ☐

Pass the book to Jokester 2! ➡

How do you spy on insects?

You have to BUG their phone!

C
LAUC

What's the best milk to drink?

My favorite is LEGEND-dairy!

C
LAUC

What is the most literate vegetable?

A READ pepper.

C
LAUC

What state holds the most animals?

Noah's Ark-ansas!

C
LAUC

 # JOKESTER 2

What do desert animals sleep on?

Armadillo pillows!

☐ LAUGH

Why can't the ocean drive a car?

It keeps crashing into the beach.

☐ LAUGH

Which state asks the most questions?

WHY-oming!

☐ LAUGH

What kind of bird helps the blind?

A SEE-gull.

☐ LAUGH

Time to add up your points! ➝

SCORE BOARD

Add up each Jokester's laugh points
for this round!

JOKESTER 1

$$\frac{}{\text{Total}} \big/ 8$$

JOKESTER 2

$$\frac{}{\text{Total}} \big/ 8$$

ROUND WINNER

ROUND
9

Why were the buckets good at golf?

They had a hole-in-one.

 LAUGH

Why did the grape enter the race?

He was feeling juiced.

 LAUGH

Why was the ruler always first in line?

She kept inching ahead.

 LAUG

Why did the phone change its name?

The new one had a nice RING to it.

LAUG

 **JOKESTER 1**

What do wood boards do for fun?

They make PLANK calls!

 LAUGH

What did the couch say, when the chair asked how his day was going?

"SOFA-r so good!"

LAUGH

Why can't you have a birthday party at the library?

They're always booked!

LAUGH

Where did the artist draw most of her shadows?

In the shade!

LAUGH

Pass the book to Jokester 2! ➜

Knock Knock.
Who's there?
Cheese.
Cheese, who?
Cheese, you're suspicious!
Open up!

LAUGH

How do you know if a
fish statue is life-size?

They are always made to SCALE!

LAUGH

Why did the beekeeper call
the doctor?

He had a case of HIVES!

LAUG

What is a king's favorite
measuring tool?

A ruler!

LAUG

What is the best way to reward a dog, for good behavior?

Give him a round of a-PAWS!

○ LAUGH

Who is the baseball player's favorite superhero?

BAT-man!

○ LAUGH

What's the name of the famous bird composer?

Johann Sebastian BAWK!

○ LAUGH

Why did the judge not let the golfer play?

The ball was in her court.

○ LAUGH

Time to add up your points! →

SCORE BOARD

Add up each Jokester's laugh points for this round!

JOKESTER 1

$$\frac{}{\text{Total}} \, /8$$

JOKESTER 2

$$\frac{}{\text{Total}} \, /8$$

ROUND WINNER

ROUND 10

What do you call two fights happening at the same time?

Dual duels!

LAUGH

Why do bakers always have dough?

They KNEAD it!

☐ LAUGH

Why do people not trust lemurs?

Their tall tails!

☐ LAUG

Which transportation vehicle is known to be crazy?

The LOCO-motive!

☐ LAU

What country would fish feel most at home in?
Finland!

☐ LAUGH

What beach do ghosts visit most?
Mali-BOO!

☐ LAUGH

Knock Knock.
Who's there?
Hangar.
Hangar, who?
HANGAR-round and find out!

☐ LAUGH

What does a tree use to sew?
A pine needle!

☐ LAUGH

Pass the book to Jokester 2! ➝

What did the kid say about his camping trip?

"It was in-TENTS!"

 LAUGH

Why did the lens do well in school?

It had great FOCUS!

 LAUGH

Where do you go to learn how to get on a boat, train, or airplane?

Boarding school!

 LAUG

How do you open a secret lock?

Very low-key.

 LAUC

Which two states are always asking 'why'?

WHY-oming and Ha-WHY-ii!

 LAUGH

What do you call an animal that doesn't like to share his floor space?

A GROUND-hog!

 LAUGH

Why did the teacher scold the glue sticks?

She caught them passing STICKY notes!

LAUGH

What kind of shorts does Mike Tyson wear?

BOXER shorts!

 LAUGH

Time to add up your points! →

SCORE BOARD

Add up each Jokester's laugh points for this round!

JOKESTER 1

$\dfrac{}{\text{Total}}$ /8

JOKESTER 2

$\dfrac{}{\text{Total}}$ /8

ROUND WINNER

Add up all your points from each round.
The Jokester with the most points is crowned

The Laugh Master!

In the event of a tie, continue to Round 11
- The Tie-Breaker Round!

JOKESTER 1

_____
Grand Total

JOKESTER 2

_____
Grand Total

THE LAUGH MASTER

ROUND 11

TIE-BREAKER
(Winner Takes ALL!)

What was the lemonade's favorite baseball position?

Pitcher!

LAU

Why does no one else stay at Patrick's in Bikini Bottom?

It's a 1-star hotel!

LAU

What's a ship crew's favorite candy?

Lifesavers!

LAU

How do you make road trips less lonely?

Adopt a highway!

LAU

What do millionaires and pizza have in common?

They both have a lot of dough!

LAUGH

Why do Eskimos always take a chisel with them on first dates?

It makes it easier to break the ice!

LAUGH

What do you use to hold together an ice fort?

Ig-GLUE.

LAUGH

Why was one windmill waving at the other?

He was a big FAN!

LAUGH

Pass the book to Jokester 2! →

 **JOKESTER 2**

Why did the crow never get in any accidents?

He was always very CAW-tious!

LAUGH

Why did the chicken go on vacation?

She was tired of being cooped up!

LAUGH

Why did the quarterback paint the football like a rainbow?

So he could pass with flying colors!

LAUG

Did you hear about the boy who pretended to be a soccer ball?

He got a good KICK out of it!

LAUC

Why did the horse get a job at the rodeo?

He wanted a STABLE income.

LAUGH

Why wouldn't the ram let the farmer sheer off his wool?

He was feeling too SHEEPISH.

LAUGH

What do you call a decent festival?

Fair.

LAUGH

What is the taxi driver's favorite vegetable?

CAB-bage!

LAUGH

Time to add up your points! →

Add up all your points from the
Tie-Breaker Round.
The Jokester with the most points is crowned

The Laugh Master!

JOKESTER 1 ___/8
Total

JOKESTER 2 ___/8
Total

_____
THE LAUGH MASTER

Check out our

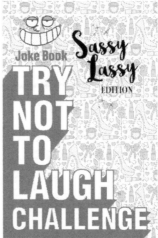

Visit our Amazon Store at:

other joke books!

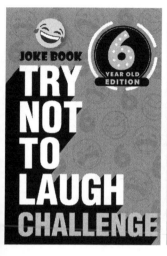 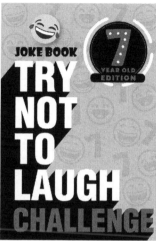 

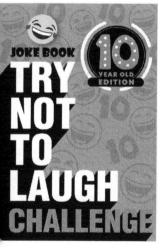 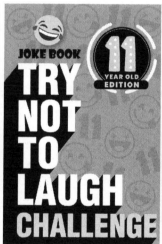 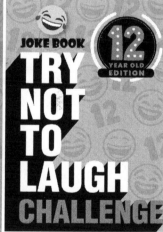

Made in the USA
Middletown, DE
30 October 2019